DIG DEEP! DIG DEEP! ARE THERE ANY DINO BONES THAT PEEP?

Created and Written
By Grenville Solomon and Vinita Deshpande
Illustrated by Anne Angelshaug

One day, Venda was sent to dig dinosaur bones for the science museum. Venda is a strong robot. He could dig really deep to find dino bones. He trudged up the mountain to find the spot. The spot was marked with a red flag.

TODAYS SPECIAL

ATOMIC SHAKE AND MICROCHIP BURGER

"Dig Deep! Dig Deep! Are there any dino bones that peep?" Venda sang to himself as he dug 5 feet. He could not see any dino bones peeping.

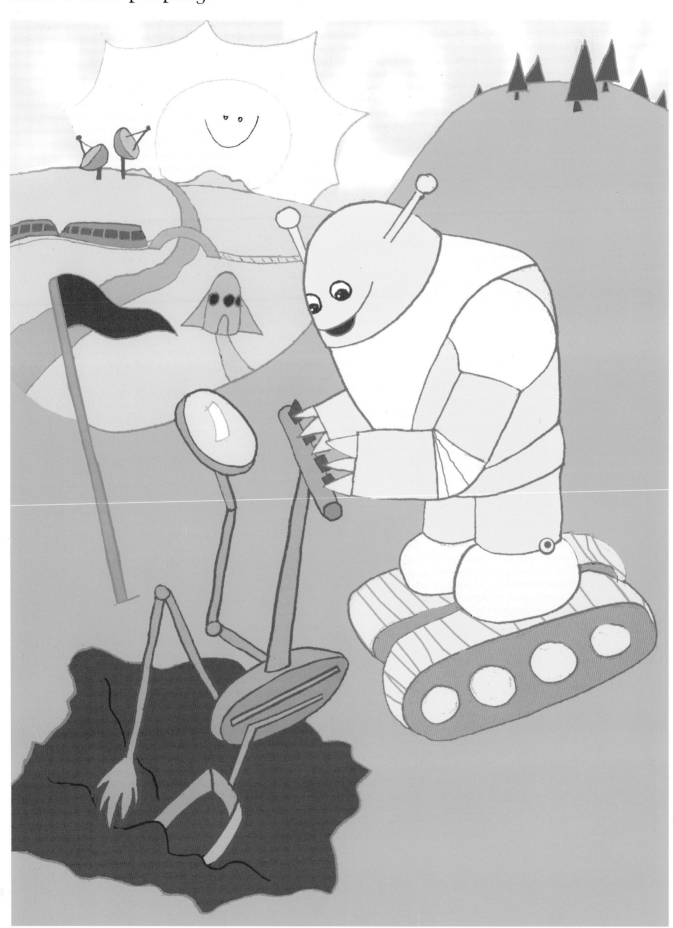

Just then Dakku the cunning robot walked past. "Why are you digging?" asked Dakku.

"I am digging for dino bones," replied Venda. "Well," said Dakku cheekily, "you are digging in the wrong spot."

Dakku wanted to confuse Venda. "That's the right spot," he said, pointing to a spot a few yards away from where Venda was digging.

Venda quietly stopped digging. He went to the new spot and started digging again.

"Dig Deep! Dig Deep! Are there any dino bones that peep?" he continued to sing as he dug another 10 feet. But there were no dino bones peeping.

As he was digging Anjuda came along. "You are digging!" he exclaimed. "How exciting! What are you looking for?" "Dino bones," replied Venda.

"That's the wrong spot," retorted Anjuda. "The ground is soft. If there were any dino bones, they would have crumbled to dust, and would not be worth digging up. This is the perfect spot. Its hard and rocky. Any dino bones would be well preserved."

"He seems to know what he is talking about," Venda thought to himself. He came out from where he had been digging and started digging at the new spot.

"Dig Deep! Dig Deep! Are there any dino bones that peep?" He went on, as he dug another 15 feet. He was tired and exhausted. But there were no dino bones peeping.

Just then, Goody came along. He was shocked to see that Venda had dug so many holes. "What happened Venda? Why have you made so many holes? Have you found any dino bones?"

Venda replied sadly, "No. I listened to Dakku and Anjuda and started digging in the other spots, but did not find any bones."

Goody realised what had happened and told Venda, "let's take a break."

They both went to the robot snack bar to have some microchip burgers and their favourite atomic shakes. This would freshen up Venda, thought Goody.

"If only you had dug 30 feet in the spot marked with the red flag, you would have certainly found dino bones," Goody told Venda.

Both robots then went back to the spot with the red flag to continue digging. **"Dig Deep! Dig Deep! Are there any dino bones that peep?"** the two robots sang, as they dug.

Yes! Yes! They found a large dino bone peeping. The robots were very excited and danced with joy.

Goody and Venda then carried the dino bones to the science museum.